DC Thomson

Published in Great Britain by
D.C. Thomson & Co., Ltd,
185 Fleet Street, London, EC4A 2HS.
© D.C. Thomson & Co., Ltd, 2011.

CONTACT DETAILS By post: The Beano, D.C. Thomson & Co.,Ltd,
2 Albert Square, Dundee DD1 9QJ
email: beano@dcthomson.co.uk
phone: 01382 223131

PROMOTIONS promotions@dcthomson.co.uk
SUBSCRIPTIONS subscriptions@dcthomson.co.uk
SYNDICATION syndication@dcthomson.co.uk
CIRCULATION circulation@dcthomson.co.uk
LICENSING start.licensing@btinternet.com

For Advertising Please Contact:
Amy-Louise Reeves
020 7400 1047
areeves@dcthomson.co.uk

recycle
When you have finished with
this magazine please recycle it.

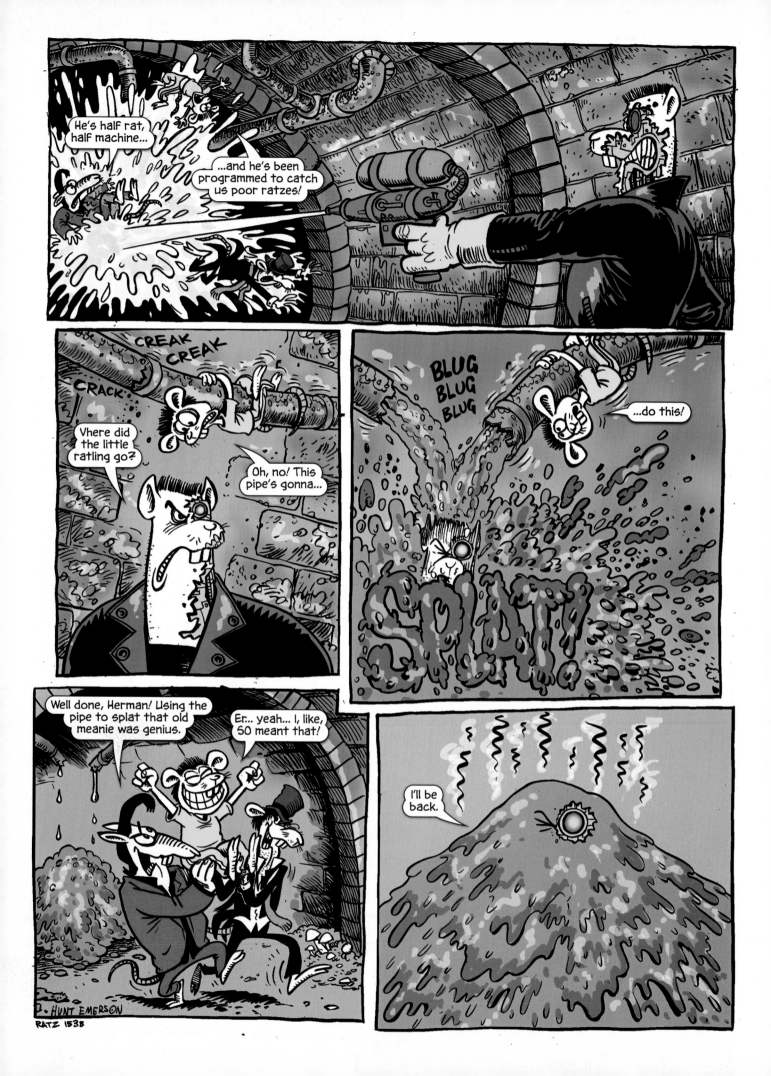

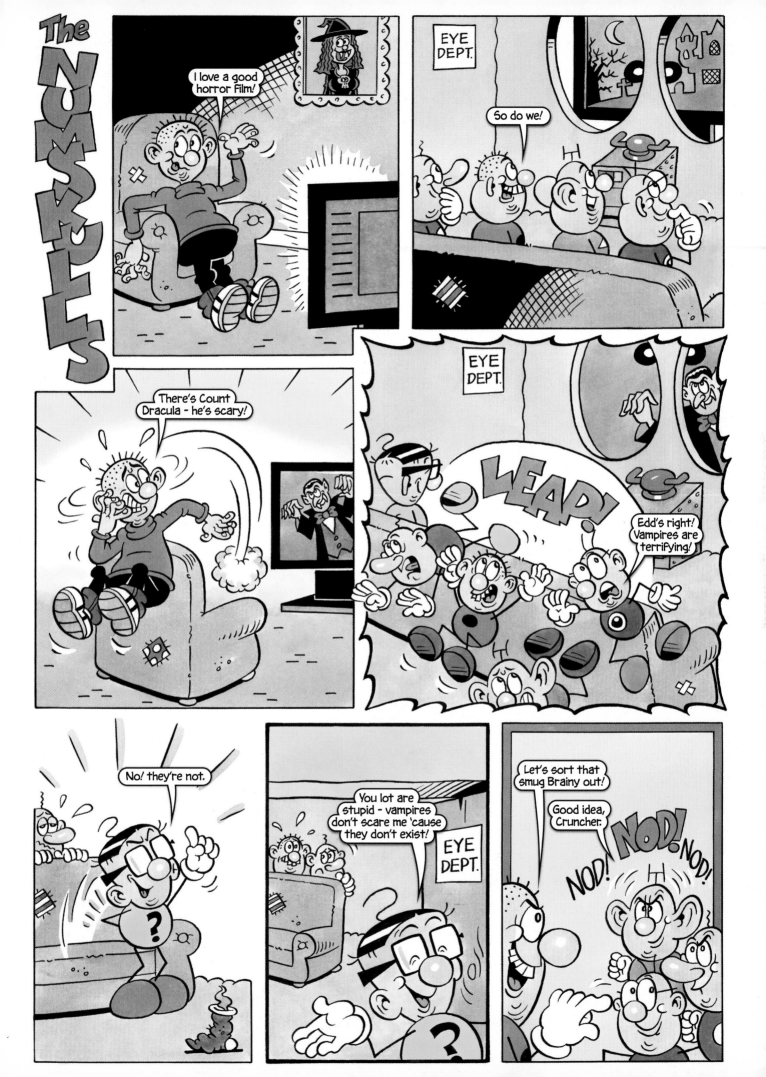

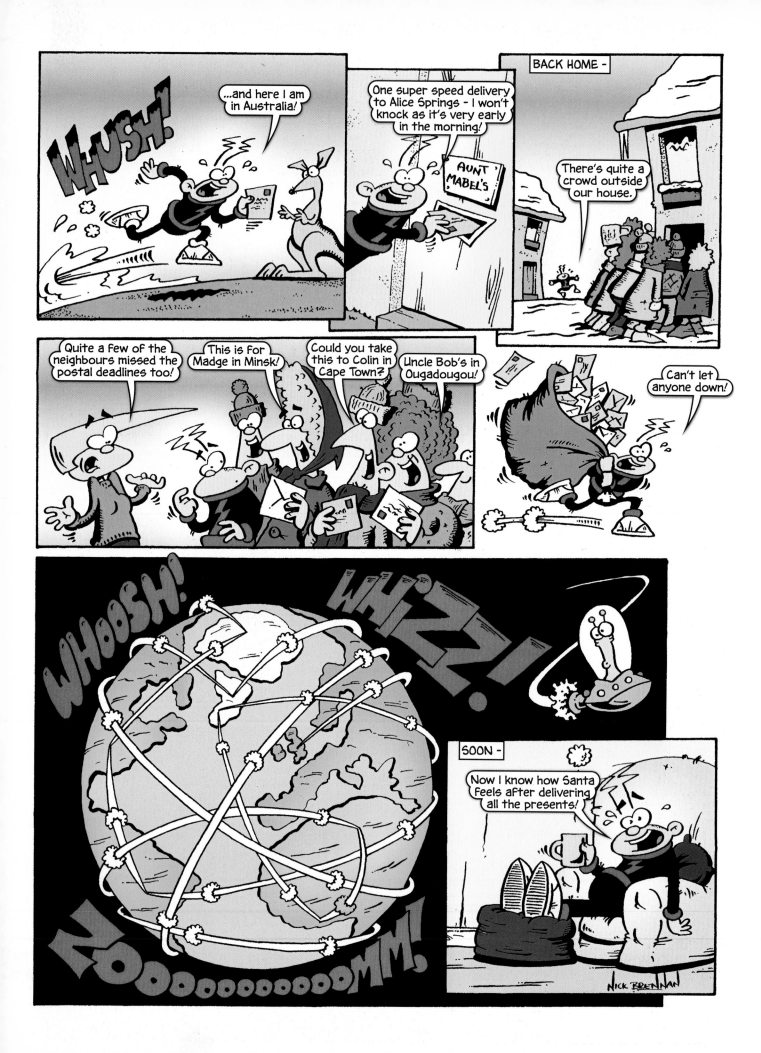

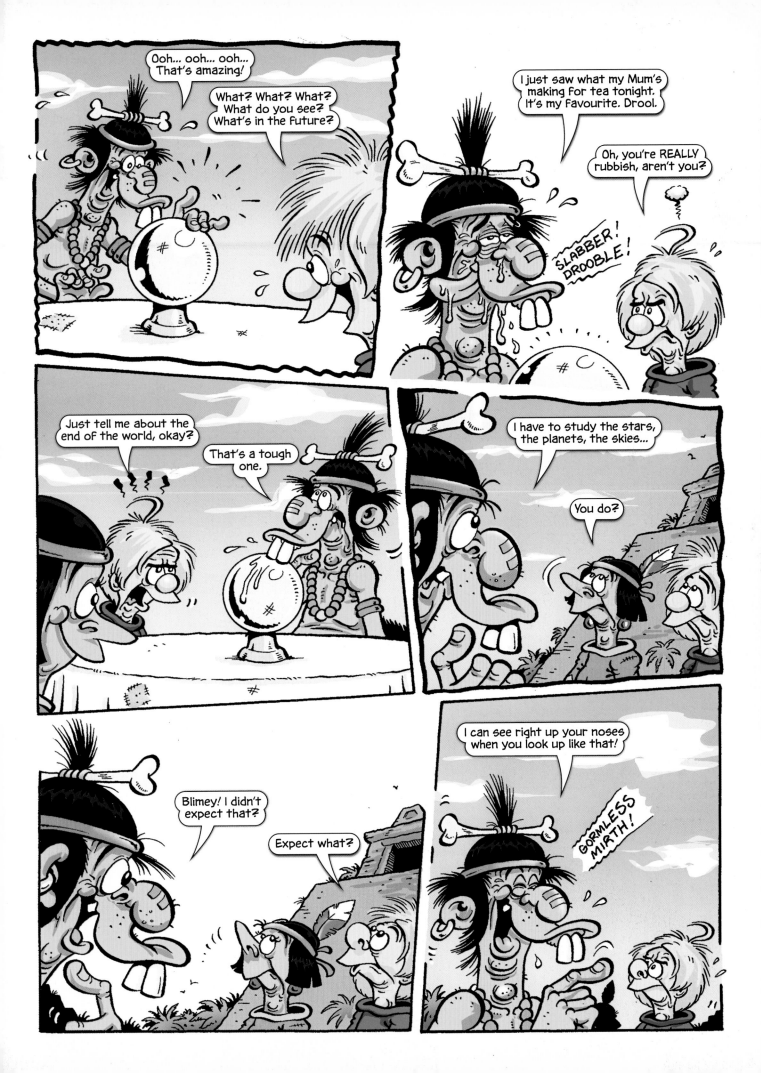

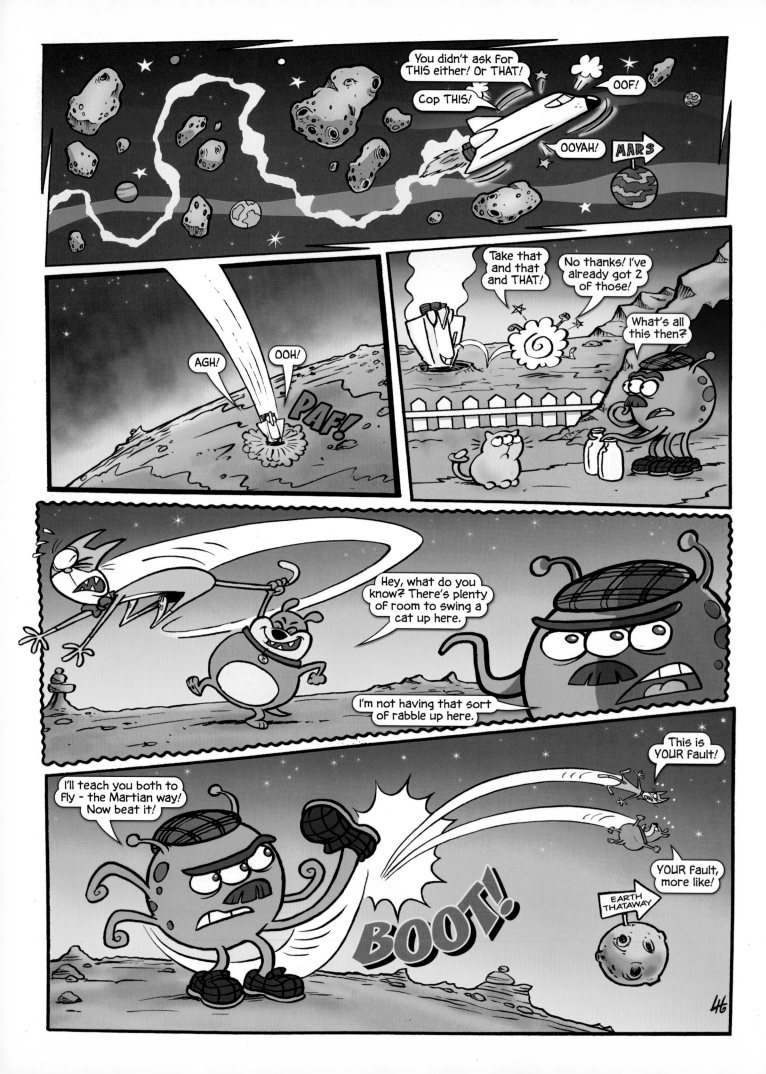

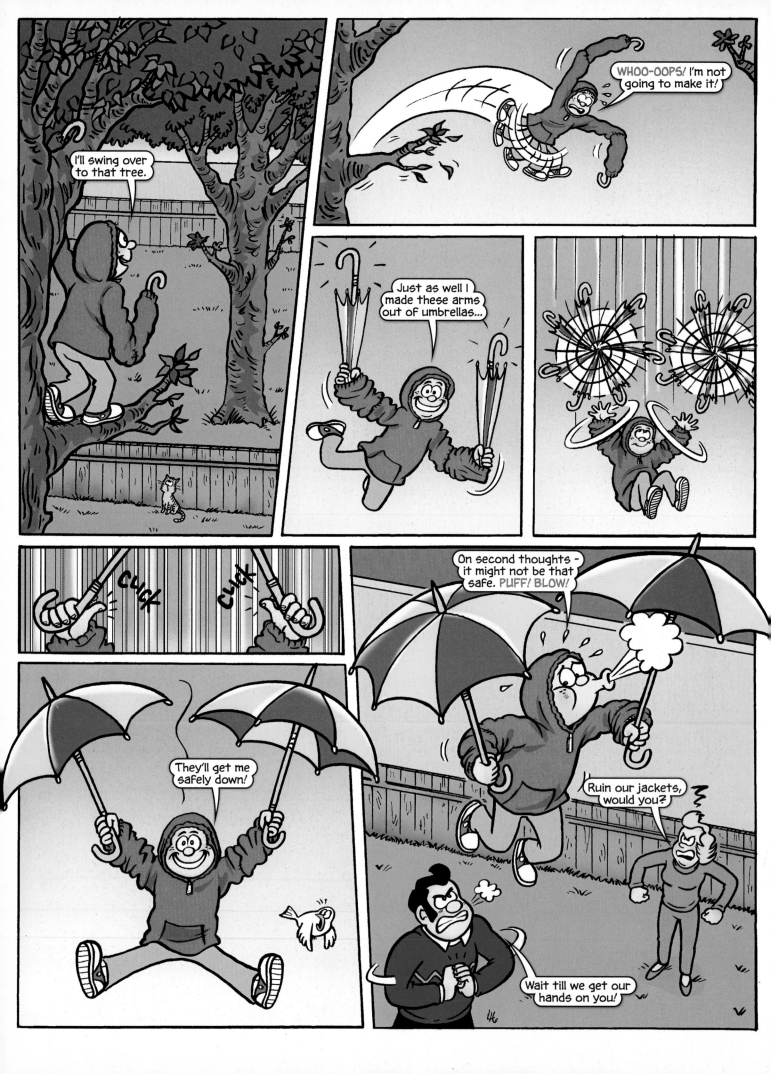

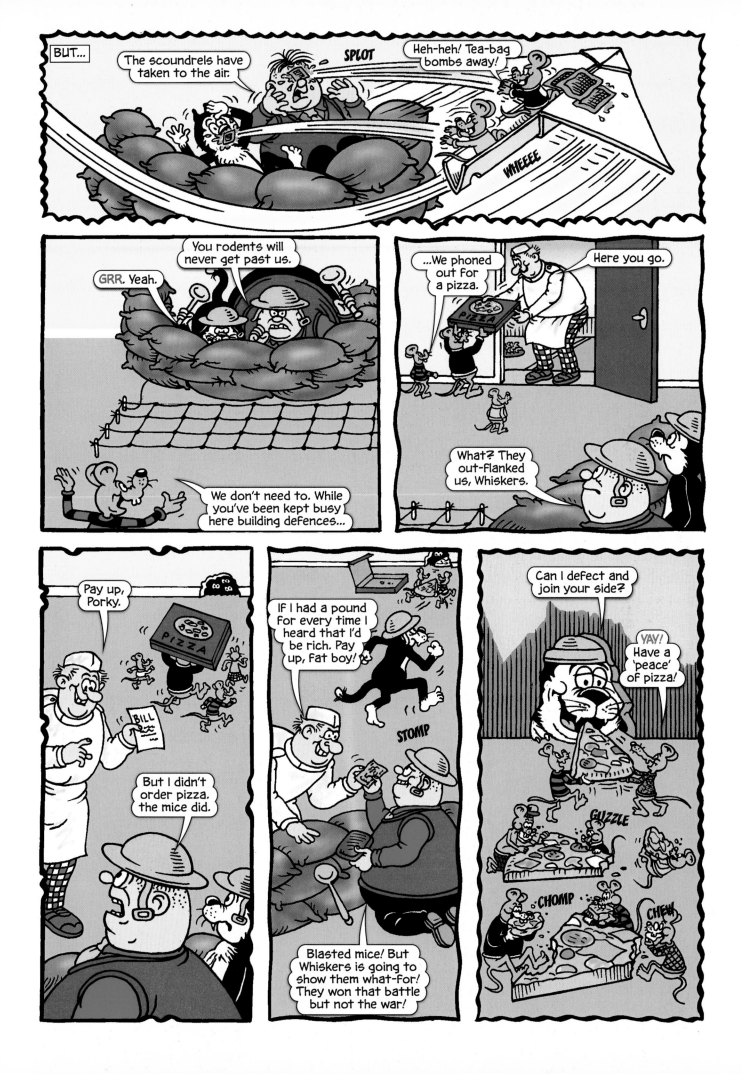

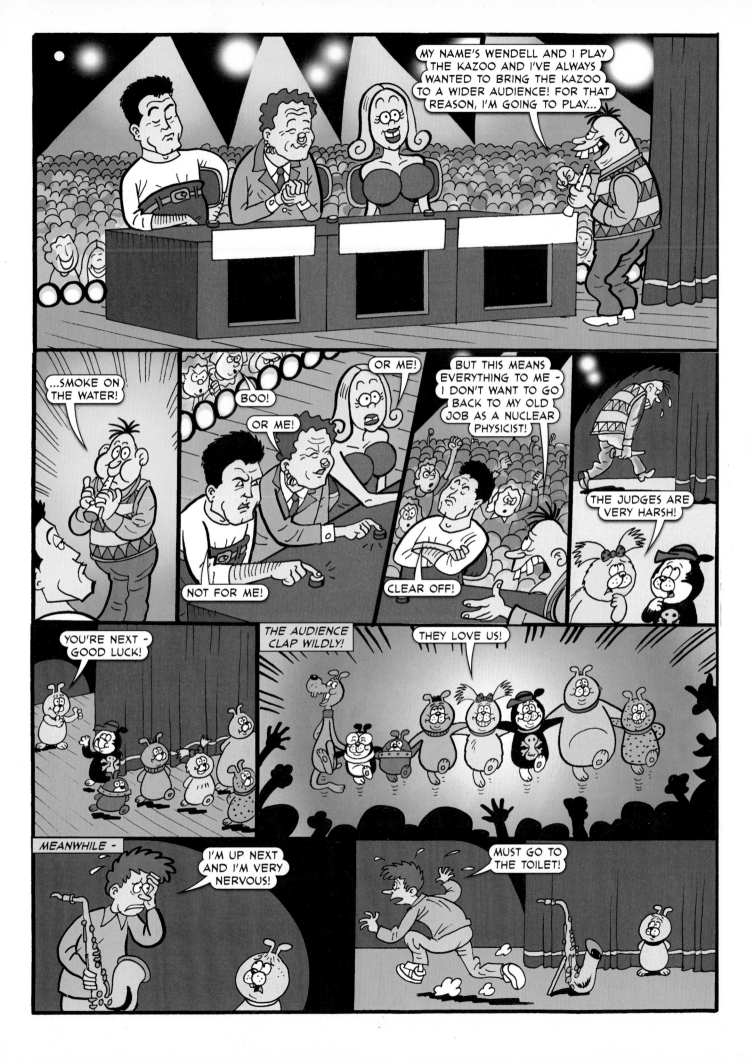

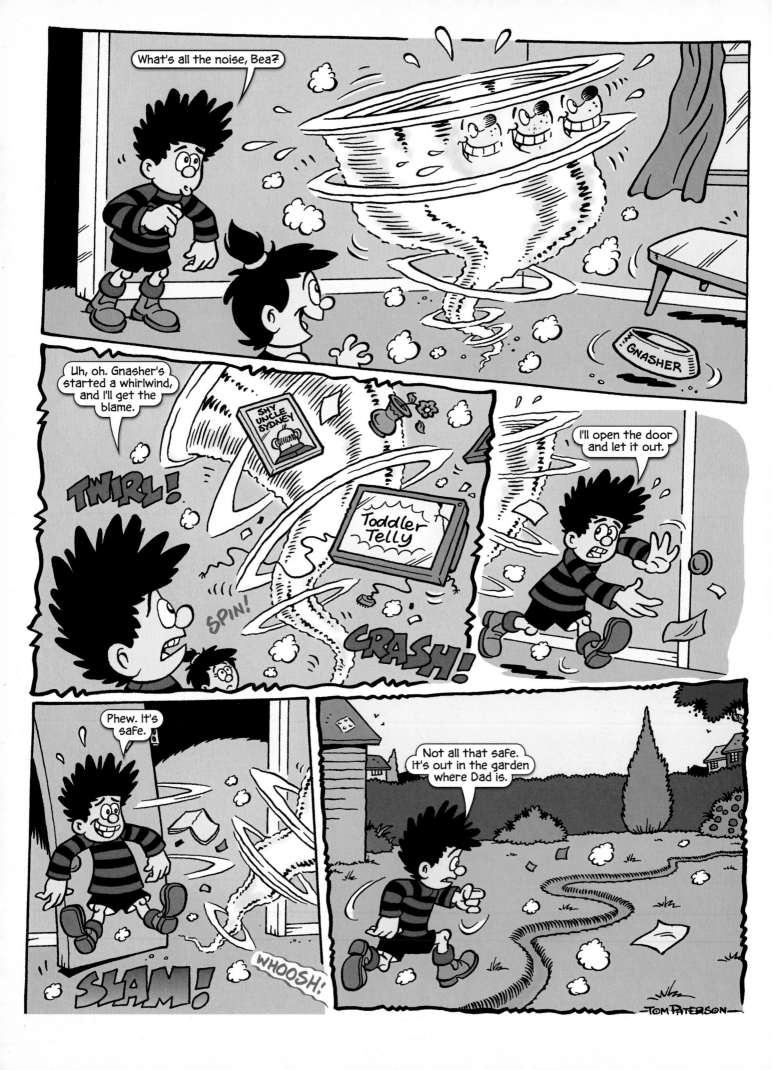

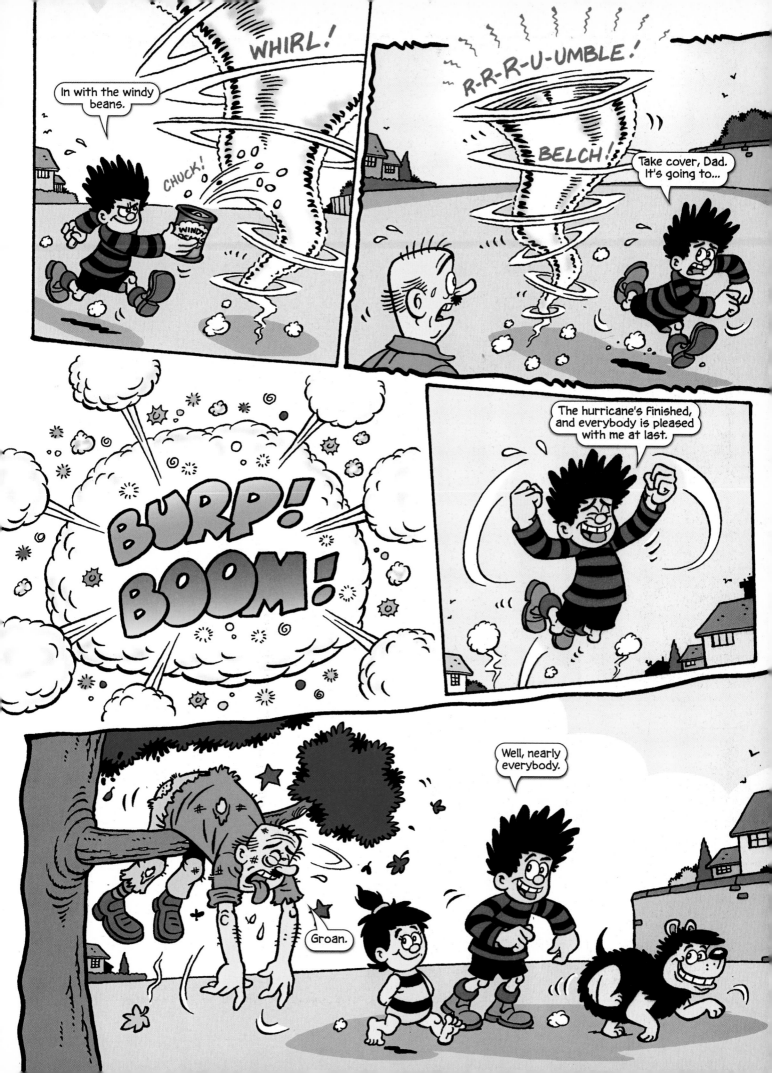